THE MAN IN THE E

Look at the man standing
near the car.
He is giving the other
man a lot of money.
The man on the pavement is
saying, 'Thank you.'
The two men are smiling.

Now the man is getting into the car.
It is his car.
He is very happy.
He is smiling.
It is a big car.
It can go very fast.

Now the man is driving the car.
The car is very, very big.
The car is blue and the seats are blue, too.
The paint is shining.
The wheels are white.
Can you see the lights?
Point to the number of the car.
Can you read it?

Now the man is driving the car very fast.
He is smiling.
He is very happy.
He is not looking in front of the car.
He is looking behind.
He is very careless.
Look at the hens and the ducks.
They are running and jumping.

The car is going very fast.
There is a cat in front of
the car.
The man is not looking behind
now.
He is looking in front.
He can see the cat.
Is he stopping?
Is he smiling?

Look at the cat!
It is jumping up.
Cats can jump.
This cat is jumping up
into a tree!
It is holding one of the
branches.
The man in the car is
looking behind.
He is looking at the cat.
He is laughing.

These boys are riding bicycles.
They are riding at the side of the road.
They are not riding the bicycles carelessly.
They are being careful.

Look at the car.
It is coming along the road.
It is behind the two boys.
The man is driving fast and carelessly.
He is not looking in front of him.

The boys are not on their bicycles.
One boy is sitting in the road.
He is holding his head.
One boy is sitting on the grass at the side of the road.
He is looking at his knee.
There is a cut on his knee.
The car is not stopping.

Look at this girl.
She is walking along the side of the road.
Her dress is clean.
Her shoes are clean.
Her socks are clean.
Can you see the water in the road?

Here is the big car.
The driver can see the water.
He is not stopping.
He is not going slowly.
He is not going around the water.
The front wheel of the car is going into the water.

Look at the water!
The water is going over the girl.

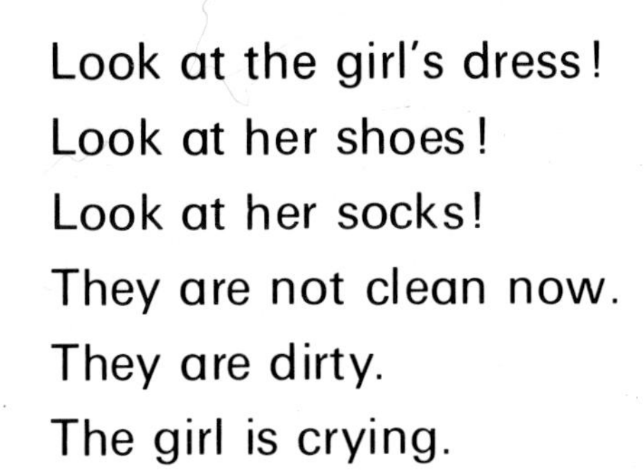

Look at the girl's dress!
Look at her shoes!
Look at her socks!
They are not clean now.
They are dirty.
The girl is crying.

The man in the car is not looking behind.
He is not stopping.
He is not helping the girl.
He is smiling.
The girl is unhappy but the man in the car is happy.

This man is sitting on a seat by the road.
He has a newspaper in his hand but he is not reading it.
The sun is shining.
It is hot.
The man's hat is over his eyes.
He is asleep.
There is a dog by the side of the seat.
His dog is sleeping, too.
There is a tree behind the seat and there are some birds in the tree.
They are singing.

Look at the seat now!

The man is not sleeping.

He is not sitting down.

He is on his feet.

He is jumping up and down and shouting.

He is holding up his arms.

He is shouting at the driver of the car.

The birds are not singing but the dog is barking.

There is a lot of noise!

Look at all the people.
This is a picnic.
Can you see the fire?
Can you see the smoke?
The man is cooking some meat over the fire.
The woman is helping him.
The girl is putting a table-cloth on the grass.
One boy is putting some plates on the cloth.
Another boy is putting some knives and spoons on the cloth.
The car is coming.
Can you see it?

Look at the smoke!

Look at the fire!

The man's face is dirty.

His shirt is dirty.

The woman's face is dirty,

Her dress is dirty.

The table-cloth is dirty.

The children's faces are dirty.

The meat is in the fire.

There is nothing to eat.

They cannot have their picnic.

They are all very unhappy.

What is the man doing?
He is painting the top of
his shop.
He is painting it red.
He is standing on a ladder.
The foot of the ladder is
near the side of the road.
Can you see the car?
It is going very fast.
The man is driving very carelessly.

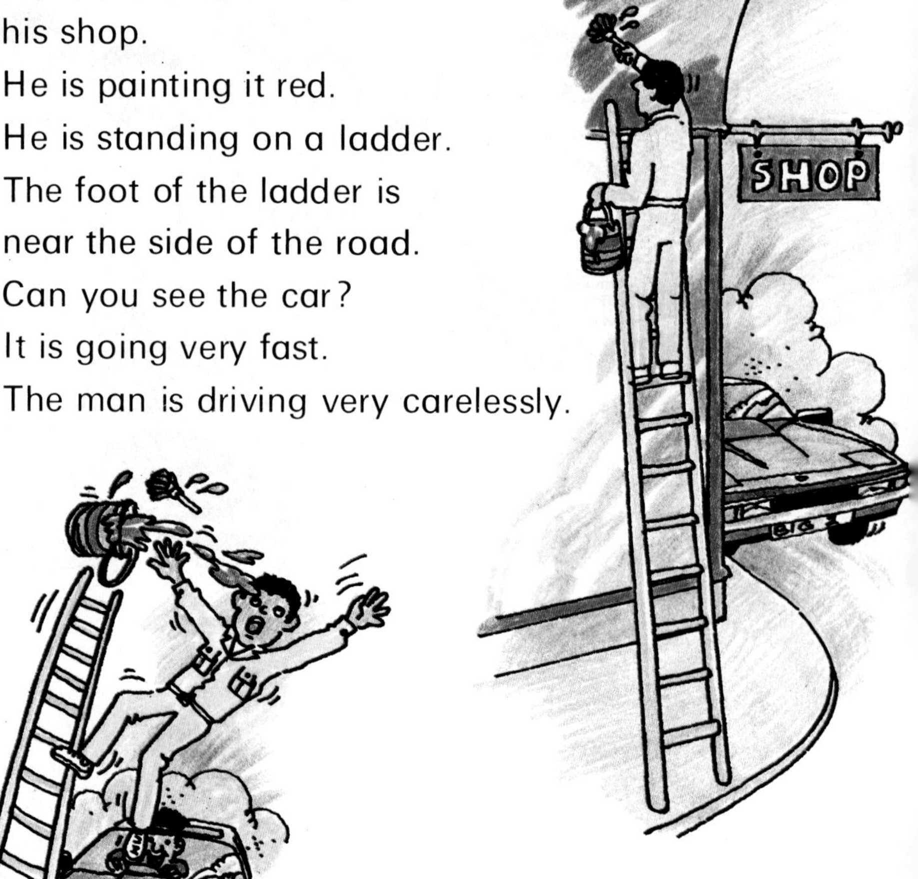

The wheel of the car is knockin
the foot of the ladder.
The man is falling down.
The tin of paint is falling
on him.
The car is not stopping.
The driver is laughing.

The woman is looking at the shop window.
She is carrying a big basket.
In the basket there are
a box of matches,
a bag of rice,
a tin of soup,
a bag of sugar,
a packet of tea,
a tin of coffee and some bread.

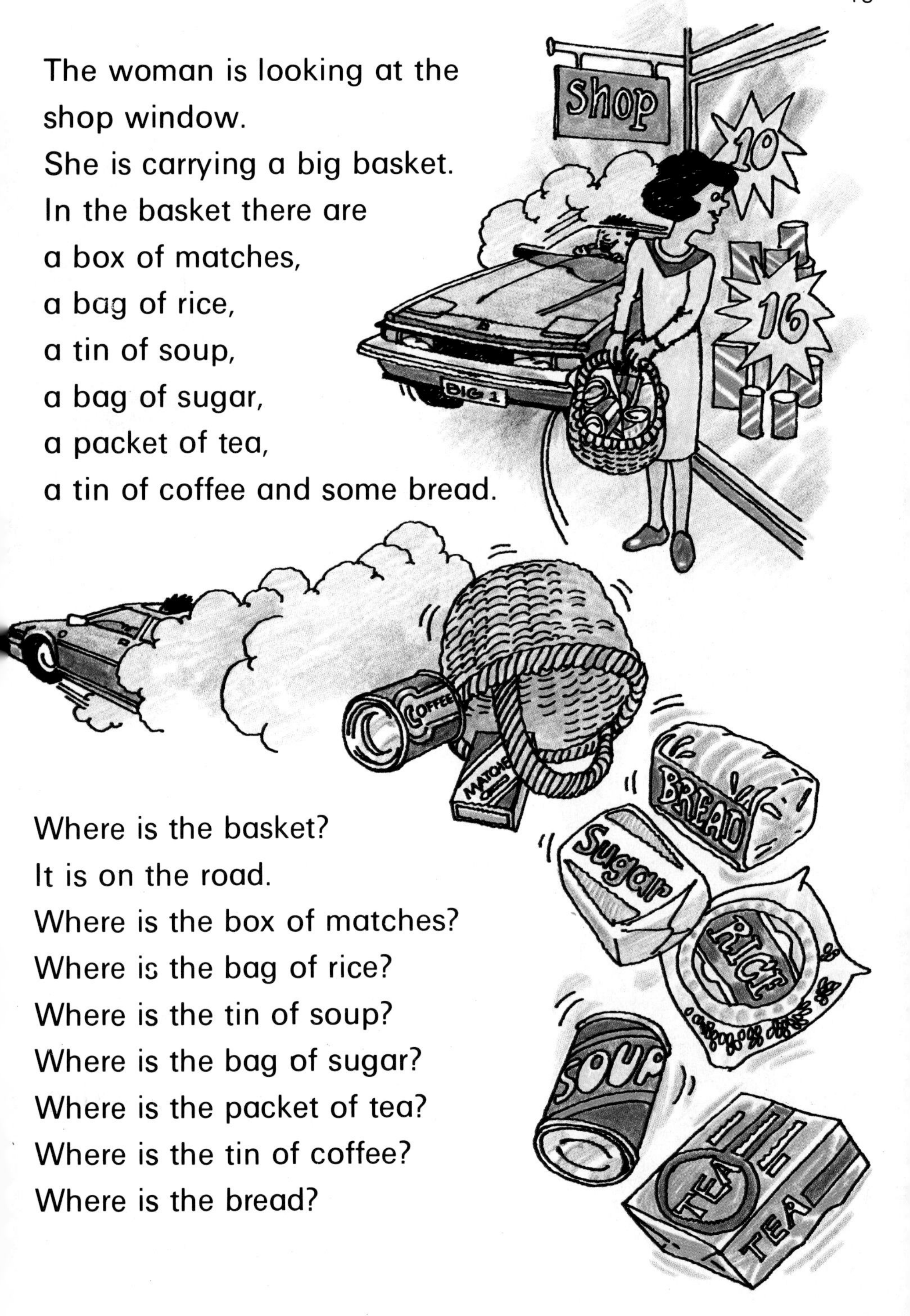

Where is the basket?
It is on the road.
Where is the box of matches?
Where is the bag of rice?
Where is the tin of soup?
Where is the bag of sugar?
Where is the packet of tea?
Where is the tin of coffee?
Where is the bread?

The driver is looking back.
He is laughing at the woman.
He is not looking in front.
There is a tree in front of the car.
The car is going very fast.
The man cannot see the tree.

Now the man can see the tree.
He is not laughing now.
He is shouting.
He is turning the wheel.
The car is turning.
The side of the car is knocking the tree.
Can you see the river?

Now the car is in the river.
There is water in the car.
We cannot see the wheels.
They are under the water.
The car is not going fast now!
Look at the people!
They are looking at the man in the car
and they are laughing.

Now all the people are talking to a policeman, and the policeman is talking to the man.
'You are very careless,' he is saying.
'You are a bad driver.
What is your name?
Where do you live?'
The policeman is writing in his book.
The driver of the big car is very wet and very unhappy.

QUESTIONS AND EXERCISES

Page 1

1 What is the man near the car giving the man on the pavement?
2 What is the man on the pavement saying?
3 Are they smiling?
4 Is it a big car?
5 Is it fast or slow?

Page 2

1 What is the man doing?
2 How many seats are there in the car?
3 What colour is the car?
4 What colour are the wheels?
5 Point to the lights.
6 What is the car's number?

Page 3

1 Is the man driving very slowly?
2 Is he smiling?
3 Is he unhappy?
4 Is he looking in front?
5 What are the hens and ducks doing?

Page 4

1 What is in front of the car?
2 Can the man see the cat?
3 Look at the picture at the bottom of the page.
What is the cat doing?
4 What is the man in the car doing?

Page 5

1 How many boys are there?
2 What are they riding?
3 Are they riding them carelessly?
4 Finish this: 'The man is driving fast and . . . .
He is not . . . .'
5 Look at the bottom of the page. Finish this: 'One boy is sitting in . . . and one boy is . . . .'
6 Finish this: 'There is . . . on one boy's knee.'
7 Is the car stopping?

Page 6

1 Where is the girl walking?
2 Finish this: 'Her dress, her shoes and her socks are . . . .'
3 Is there any water in the road?
4 Can the driver see the water?
5 Is he going around the water?
6 Where is the front wheel of the car going?

Page 7

1 Where is the water going?
2 Finish this: 'The girl's dress, shoes . . . dirty.'
3 Who is crying?
4 Who is smiling?
5 Who is happy?
6 Who is unhappy?

Page 8

1 What is the man sitting on?
2 Is he reading the newspaper?
3 Is the sun shining?
4 Where is the man's hat?
5 Where is the dog?
6 What is the dog doing?
7 Where is the tree?
8 Where are the birds?
9 What are the birds doing?

Page 9

1 Is the man sleeping?
2 What is he doing?
3 What is the dog doing?
4 How much noise is there?

Page 10

1 What is this?

2 Point to the fire.
3 Point to the smoke.
4 What is the man doing?
5 What is the woman doing?
6 What is the girl doing?
7 What is one boy doing?
8 What is the other boy doing?

Page 11

1 What is dirty?
2 Where is the meat?
3 Is there anything to eat?
4 Who is unhappy?

Page 12

1 What is the man painting?
2 What is he standing on?
3 Where is the foot of the ladder?
4 Is the man driving carefully?
5 Look at the bottom of the page.
What is the wheel doing?
6 What is the man doing?
7 What is the tin of paint doing?
8 What is the driver doing?

Page 13

1 What is the woman looking at?
2 What is she carrying?

3 What is there in the basket?
4 Look at the bottom of the page. Where is the basket?
5 Finish this: 'On the road there a . . . of matches,
a . . . of rice, a . . . of soup, a . . . of sugar,
a . . . of tea, a . . . of coffee and . . . bread.'

Page 14

1 Look at the top of the page. What is the driver doing?
2 Where is the tree?
3 Can the driver see the tree?
4 Look at the bottom of the page. Is the driver laughing?
5 What is he doing?
6 Is the car turning?
7 Is the car knocking the tree?
8 Point to the river.

Page 15

1 Where is the car?
2 What is in the car?
3 Where are the wheels of the car?
4 What are all the people doing?

Page 16

1 What are all the people doing?
2 What is the policeman doing?
3 Who is very wet and unhappy?

WORDS IN THIS BOOK

around | asleep | a bag | barking

a basket | a bicycle | a bird | a box

a branch | bread | careful writing | careless writing

a cat | coffee | cooking | crying

a clean dress

a dirty dress

The driver is driving.

a cut

a dog

a duck

a fire

falling down

grass

a hat

a hen

jumping

a knee

a knife

knocking

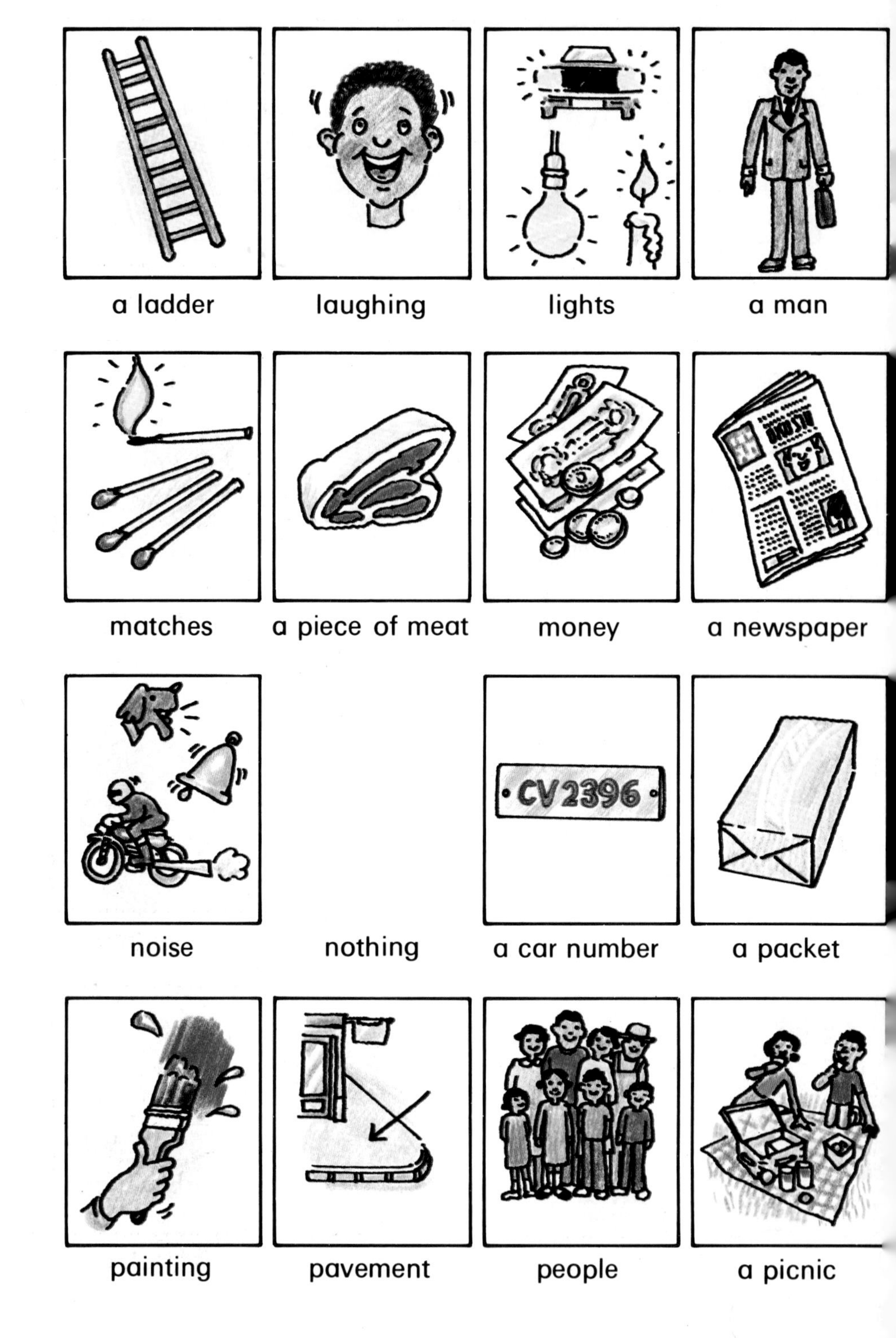

a ladder
laughing
lights
a man
matches
a piece of meat
money
a newspaper
noise
nothing
a car number
a packet
painting
pavement
people
a picnic

RICE
a plate
rice
riding
a river
a road
running
a seat
shining
SHOP
a shirt
a shoe
a shop window
shouting
SONGS
singing
sleeping
smiling
smoke

socks
soup
a spoon
standing
SUGAR
SUGAR
Tea
stopping
sugar
a table-cloth
tea
a tin
a tree
turning
unhappy
water
wet
a wheel
a woman

Start with English Readers

Grade 1
Po-Po
Mary and her Basket
A New Tooth
Pat and her Picture
The Kite

Grade 2
Peter and his Book
John and Paul go to School
The Bird and the Bread
Two Stories
Tonk and his Friends

Grade 3
Sam's Ball
The Fox and the Stork/The Bird and the Glass
The Big Race
The Man in the Big Car
The Queen's Handkerchief

Grade 4
Nine Stories About People
Four Clever People
In the Cave
An Apple for the Monkey

Grade 5
People and Things
Doctor Know It All/The Brave Little Tailor
The Flyer

Grade 6
The Bottle Imp
The World Around Us

Start with English Readers are also available on cassette.

Start with Words and Pictures

This alphabetical picture dictionary provides extra help for Grades 1 to 3. It has been specially written for use with *Start with English* materials.

For practice using the words in the picture dictionary, there is the *Start with Words and Pictures Activity Book.*

Oxford University Press
Great Clarendon Street, Oxford OX2 6DP

Oxford New York
Athens Auckland Bangkok Bogotá Buenos Aires
Calcutta Cape Town Chennai Dar es Salaam
Delhi Florence Hong Kong Istanbul Karachi
Kuala Lumpur Madrid Melbourne Mexico City
Mumbai Nairobi Paris São Paulo Singapore
Taipei Tokyo Toronto Warsaw

and associated companies in
Berlin Ibadan

OXFORD and OXFORD ENGLISH are trade marks
of Oxford University Press

ISBN 0 19 433549 6

First published 1983
Seventeenth impression 1999

Illustrated by Barry Rowe

Printed in China